Food Labelling

A Companion to *Food Tables*

Arnold E Bender
Emeritus Professor of Nutrition
Queen Elizabeth College
University of London

David A Bender
Lecturer in Biochemistry
University College and Middlesex School of Medicine
University College London

Oxford University Press

Oxford University Press, Walton Street, Oxford OX2 6DP

Oxford New York Toronto
Delhi Bombay Calcutta Madras Karachi
Petaling Jaya Singapore Hong Kong Tokyo
Nairobi Dar es Salaam Cape Town
Melbourne Auckland

and associated companies in
Berlin Ibadan

ISBN 0 19 832785 4

Acknowledgement

The figures in Table 6 have been calculated from figures in
sections 1 and 3 of *The Composition of Foods*, 4th edn, A.A.
Paul & D.A.T. Southgate, HMSO, London,1978, and are
reproduced with the permission of the Controller of Her
Majesty's Stationery Office.

Typeset by Mike Brain, Oxford
Printed in Great Britain

Contents

Preface

This book is a companion to *Food Tables*, which dealt largely with the nutrient composition of common foods.

Food Labelling provides the information needed to read nutritional labels on packaged foods : a list of permitted food additives, the basis of food labelling legislation (with examples of nutritional labelling of foods), and a glossary of nutritional and food terms likely to be found on labels and elsewhere. In addition, it gives a detailed analysis of the types of fats present in foods listed in *Food Tables*.

Food legislation

The first general food laws in the world were passed in Britain in 1860. Before that, there had been laws relating specifically to certain foods such as bread, but otherwise little control over the composition, quality and adulteration of foods.

Over the years, these laws have been expanded and modified, and currently we are operating under the Food Safety Act 1990 and European Community Directives. The regulations include three main points:

● It is an offence to sell for human consumption any food to which substances have been added or subtracted or which has been processed so as to render it injurious to health.

● It is an offence to sell food which is not of the nature, substance or quality demanded or expected by the purchaser or to label or advertise food with a false or misleading description – hence the shopkeeper shares with the manufacturer responsibility for ensuring that the food is as might be expected from the description.

● It is an offence to sell food which is unfit for human consumption.

The Laws are passed by Parliament, and enforced by Local Authorities, through the Trading Standards Officers and Environmental Health Oficers. In addition, there are specific regulations covering particular foods, processes and additives, and foods are also subject to Acts of Parliament dealing with Fair Trading, Weights and Measures and other Consumer Protection Legislation.

Food labelling

The regulations concerning labelling of foods apply to all foods ready for delivery to the ultimate consumer, and also to foods for catering establishments, but not to food intended for immediate consumption on the premises where it is sold.

The label must bear the *name* of the food, a *quantity statement*, a *date mark*, an *ingredient list* and any special storage conditions or conditions of use, together with the *name and address* of the manufacturer, packager or importer. Increasingly, packages of foods (and most other commodities) also have *bar codes*. This is a computer-readable label which identifies the product, the manufacturer and the package size in a numerical code. Such bar codes have allowed the automation of stock-keeping and checkouts in shops, and avoid the possibility of mistakes in entering prices into cash registers, as well as providing a detailed bill with every item named.

The *ingredients* must be listed in descending order by weight (i.e. the major ingredient must come first). Water added to a product must be declared if it constitutes more than 5% by weight of the finished product. Additives must be declared in the list. Certain foods, however, do *not* need to bear a list of ingredients; these include fresh fruit and vegetables, fortified flour, foods consisting of a single ingredient, and certain fermented foods with no added ingredients other than enzymes and cultures used to ferment them.

Nearly all pre-packaged foods are required to carry *date-marking* - a date up to and including which the food can reasonably be expected to retain its essential qualities if stored properly. If special storage conditions are required, these must be stated close to the date mark.

For foods with a shelf life of up to 12 weeks, the date-marking reads 'best before day, month, year'. Perishable foods with a shelf life of less than a month may have a 'sell by' date instead, together with advice on how soon after purchase they should be consumed, or a simple 'eat by' or 'use by' date showing the date after which they may be subject to spoilage or not be fit for consumption. It is illegal to sell a product after its 'use by' date. For foods with a longer shelf life date marking reads 'best before end of month, year'.

Frozen foods and ice cream carry star markings, which correspond to the star markings on freezers and frozen food compartments of refrigerators.

Table 1 Storage times for frozen foods and ice cream

	Temperature		Storage time	
	°C	°F	Frozen food	Ice cream
*	-4	25	1 week	1 day
**	-11	12	1 month	1 week
***	-18	0	3 months	1 month

(Longer storage of ice cream does not render it unfit to eat, but changes its texture.)

Claims and misleading descriptions

There are no restrictions on the sale of any food so long as it does not transgress any of the regulations listed above. What is controlled by law is any *claim*. Claims may be made on advertisements of various kinds, as well as leaflets and labels. In addition to the legislation there are voluntary Codes of Practice.

It is an offence to label or advertise a food so as to describe it falsely, or in such a way as to mislead as to its nature, substance or quality - quality here includes nutritional value. There are also specific controls dealing with claims for energy, calories, proteins, vitamins and minerals, slimming claims, tonic and restorative claims and any claims relating to the medicinal value of a food.

The basic principle of control for all these specific types of claims is that they must be justified and accompanied by adequate information.

Foods for particular nutritional uses

A food that has been manufactured to fulfil the requirements of a particular group of people (e.g. those with diabetes, babies, etc.) must carry on its label an indication of its special nutritional characteristics and the particular aspect of its composition, or of the manufacturing process, which makes it suitable for the intended consumer.

It is illegal to claim on the label or in an advertisement that a food is capable of preventing, treating or curing a disease unless it has a specific Product Licence under the Medicines Act for use for the claimed purpose. It is illegal to mislead the consumer, even if, strictly speaking, the statement is true.

Nutritional labelling

For foods intended for particular nutritional purposes or for which claims or even statements of nutrient contents are made, the Regulations require the nutritional information to be given in a prescribed form. Many manufacturers of other foods provide information in various styles with differing details. To make it easier to understand the Government has issued Guidelines, updated in January 1988, so that all packages list the information in a standard format.

The terms used are defined in the Guidelines:

Carbohydrate means any carbohydrate that is metabolised in the body (i.e. excluding dietary fibre), and includes sugars, starches and sugar alcohols such as sorbitol and xylitol.

Sugars includes all monosaccharides and disaccharides, but excludes sugar alcohols.

Poly-unsaturates means poly-unsaturated fatty acids only of the *cis* form (see page 17).

Table 2 Some examples of nutritional labelling

1 Minimum information on the label

Energy	1978 kJ / 471 kcal
Protein	6.3 g
Carbohydrate	68.6 g
Fat	21 g

2 More detail on fat content

Energy	1978 kJ / 471 kcal
Protein	6.3 g
Carbohydrate	68.6 g
Fat	21 g (of which saturates 8.3 g)

3 Full detail

Energy	1978 kJ / 471 kcal
Protein	6.3 g
Carbohydrate	68.6 g (of which sugars 13 g)
Fat	21 g (of which saturates 8.3 g)
Sodium	0.6 g
Fibre	2.9 g

4 Optional additional information

Carbohydrates	68.6 g (of which sugars 13 g, starch 50 g)
Fat	21 g (of which saturates 8.3 g, *trans* 3.2 g, poly-unsaturates 1.8 g, mono-unsaturates 6.0 g)
Vitamins	
Mineral salts	

Table 3 Some examples of labelling from food packets (with explanatory notes)

1 Baked beans with tomato sauce

Ingredients	beans, water, tomatoes, sugar, salt, modified starch [a], spirit vinegar, spices
Quantity	g / oz
Name and address of manufacturer	

[Notes : [a] Modified starch is added to thicken the tomato sauce - see *Glossary*.]

2 Grissini, bread sticks

Ingredients	wheat flour, vegetable fats [a], yeast, malt, salt
'Best before' date printed on bottom of box	
Nett weight	125 g
Name and address of manufacturer or importer	

[Notes : [a] The particular kind of fat is not specified, since it may be changed according to price and availability of different fats at different times.]

3 Orange marmalade suitable for diabetics

Ingredients	sorbitol syrup [a], oranges, gelling agent (pectin), citric acid, acidity regulator E-331 [b], colour (malt extract)

Nutritional information per 100 g

protein 0.1 g, fat 0 g, sorbitol 62 g, other carbohydrate 1.7 g, total 63.7 g (added note: 'it is the 'other carbohydrate' that a diabetic must take into account') energy value 1020 kJ / 239 kcal.

Additional information

best to eat less than 25 g of sorbitol a day [c]

not suitable for overweight diabetics [d]

do not refrigerate, store at room temperature

Quantity	g / oz

Name and address of manufacturer

[Notes : [a] Sorbitol is tolerated by diabetics because it is only slowly absorbed into the bloodstream.
[b] E-331 is sodium citrate - citric acid is E-330. The manufacturer could have listed both as names, or both as E- numbers, but has listed one by name and the other by number. The mixture of citric acid and sodium citrate forms a buffer to control acidity.
[c] In large amounts, sorbitol is a laxative, hence a warning not to eat too much.
[d] Sorbitol is metabolized like any other carbohydrate, yielding 16 kJ (4 kcal)/g]

4 Chicken stock cubes

Ingredients	salt [a], vegetable fat, monosodium glutamate [b], dehydrated chicken meat [c], beef extract, hydrolysed vegetable protein [d], chicken fat [e], dried parsley, natural flavourings, ascorbyl palmitate [f]

Quantity	g / oz

Name and address of manufacturer

[Notes : [a] Note that salt is the main ingredient.
[b] A flavour enhancer.
[c] This can be listed in the order of quantity when rehydrated.
[d] A general meaty savoury flavour.
[e] Low in the list – a small amount.
[f] A derivative of vitamin C, used as an anti-oxidant.]

5 Caramel Dessert Mix

Ingredients	sugar [a], dextrose [b], gelling agent E-407 [c], caseinate, modified starch [d], sodium bicarbonate [e], flavouring [f], E- 102, E-110, brown HT [g]

Quantity	g/oz

Name and address of manufacturer

[Notes : [a] Note that sugar is the first ingredient.
[b] An alternative name for glucose – the second ingredient.
[c] Carageenan (see *Glossary*).
[d] See *Glossary*.
[e] An acidity regulator.
[f] Unspecified.
[g] E-102 is tartrazine; E-110 is sunset yellow; brown HT is E-155. It is not clear why some colours are quoted by number, but brown HT by name.]

Food additives

An additive is defined as any substance not commonly regarded or used as a food, which is added to a food to affect its keeping properties, texture, consistency, appearance, taste, alkalinity, acidity, or to perform any other function. Legally the term 'additive' does not include nutrients added to enrich the food, or herbs and spices used as seasonings, salt or yeast.

Additives may be extracted from natural sources, synthesized in the laboratory to be chemically the same as natural materials (and hence known as 'nature-identical' compounds), or they may be synthetic compounds which do not occur in nature.

Additives can be grouped according to their uses and functions, as colours, preservatives, anti-oxidants (fat preservatives), emulsifiers, acidifying agents, humectants (to keep food moist), and for other specific purposes.

The use of additives is controlled by law. In some cases, the amounts that may be used are limited, or their use is restricted to specified foods, while other additives may be used more widely. In all cases, their use is only permitted when a need has been shown, and if they are regarded as being safe - hence the term 'permitted additives'.

When laboratory testing has revealed that a high dose or intake of a substance causes some change in experimental animals, then the total amount that is permitted from all foods in the daily diet is limited (with a large safety factor). This safe amount is termed the Acceptable Daily Intake (ADI), agreed by international bodies such as the World Health Organisation, as well as by various national government regulatory bodies. The Acceptable Daily Intake is usually one hundredth of the *highest dose that shows no effect* when tested. When no harm can be demonstrated even at very high levels of intake (very much higher than would be used in foods), then the substance may be used without any limitation, although the intensity of colour and flavour usually limit the amounts that are used in foods.

Permitted food additives have been classified according to their uses, and have been assigned serial numbers which may legally be used on food labels instead of, or as well as, their (sometimes complex) chemical names. Numbers with the prefix 'E-' are those permitted throughout the European Community and covered by specific European Community legislation. Additionally, some compounds are permitted in the United Kingdom, and some other countries, but are not covered by European Community legislation; these have numbers without the 'E-' prefix.

Table 4 Permitted food additives – the 'E-' numbers

Colouring materials : Used to make food more colourful or to replace colour lost in processing.

Organic compounds (some naturally occurring and others synthetic)

Yellow and orange colours

E-100	Curcumin (extracted from the spice turmeric)
E-101	Riboflavin (vitamin B_2)
E-102	Tartrazine
E-104	Quinoline yellow
107	Yellow 2G
E-110	Sunset yellow FCF or orange yellow S

Red colours

E-120	Cochineal or carminic acid
E-122	Carmoisine or azorubine
E-123	Amaranth
E-124	Ponceau 4R or cochineal red A
E-127	Erythrosine BS
128	Red 2G

Blue colours

E-131	Patent blue V
E-132	Indigo carmine or indigotine
133	Brilliant blue FCF

Green colours

E-140	Chlorophyll (the natural green colour of leaves)
E-141	Copper complex of chlorophyll
E-142	Green S or acid brilliant green BS

Brown and black colours

E-150	Caramel (caramel is made from sugar in the kitchen)
E-151	Black PN or brilliant black BN
E-153	Carbon black or vegetable carbon (charcoal)
154	Brown FK
155	Brown HT (chocolate brown HT)

Derivatives of carotene, some of which are precursors of vitamin A

E-160(a)	Alpha-, beta- or gamma-carotene (the pigments of many yellow and orange plants - vitamin A active)
E-160(b)	Annatto, bixin, norbixin (extracted from the seeds of a plant, *Bixa orellana*)
E-160(c)	Capsanthin or capsorubin
E-160(d)	Lycopene (the red colour of tomatoes)
E-160(e)	Beta-apo-8'-carotenal (vitamin A active)
E-160(f)	Ethyl ester of beta-apo-8'-carotenoic acid

Other plant colours

E-161(a)	Flavoxanthin
E-161(b)	Lutein
E-161(c)	Cryptoxanthin (vitamin A active)
E-161(d)	Rubixanthin
E-161(e)	Violaxanthin
E-161(f)	Rhodoxanthin
E-161(g)	Canthaxanthin
E-162	Beetroot red or betanin (the pigment of beetroot)
E-163	Anthocyanins (the pigments of many plants)

Inorganic compounds used as colours

E-170	Calcium carbonate (chalk, white, used as a base and firming agent, also as a source of calcium in enriched flour)
E-171	Titanium dioxide (white)
E-172	Iron oxides and hydroxides (rust - may be a useful source of iron in the diet)
E-173	Aluminium
E-175	Gold
E-180	Pigment rubine or lithol rubine BK

Preservatives: Compounds that protect foods against microbes which cause spoilage and food poisoning. They increase the storage life of foods.

Sorbic acid and salts

E-200	Sorbic acid
E-201	Sodium sorbate
E-202	Potassium sorbate
E-203	Calcium sorbate

Benzoic acid and salts

E-210	Benzoic acid (benzoic acid is found naturally in many fruits)
E-211	Sodium benzoate
E-212	Potassium benzoate
E-213	Calcium benzoate
E-214	Ethyl 4-hydroxybenzoate
E-215	Ethyl 4-hydroxybenzoate sodium salt
E-216	Propyl 4-hydroxybenzoate
E-217	Propyl 4-hydroxybenzoate sodium salt
E-218	Methyl 4-hydroxybenzoate
E-219	Methyl 4-hydroxybenzoate sodium salt

Sulphur dioxide and its salts

E-220	Sulphur dioxide (sulphur dioxide and its salts are especially useful to prevent browning of raw peeled potatoes as well as having anti-microbial properties)
E-221	Sodium sulphite
E-222	Sodium hydrogen sulphite
E-223	Sodium metabisulphite
E-224	Potassium metabisulphite
E-226	Calcium sulphite
E-227	Calcium hydrogen sulphite

Biphenyl and its derivatives

E-230	Biphenyl or diphenyl (biphenyl and its derivatives are used only on the outside of citrus skins)
E-231	2-Hydroxybiphenyl
E-232	Sodium biphenyl-2-yl oxide
E-233	2-(Thiazol-4-yl) benzimidazole (used on banana skins)
234	Nisin
E-239	Hexamine

Pickling salts

E-249	Potassium nitrite (a mixture of nitrates and nitrites is a traditional pickling agent for corned beef, ham and other cured meats)
E-250	Sodium nitrite
E-251	Sodium nitrate
E-252	Potassium nitrate (saltpetre)

Acids and their salts: Used as flavourings and as buffers to control the acidity of foods, in addition to their anti-microbial properties

E-260	Acetic acid (vinegar is a 5% solution of acetic acid)
E-261	Potassium acetate
E-262	Potassium hydrogen diacetate
262	Sodium acetate
E-263	Calcium acetate (used as a firming agent and as a source of calcium in quick-setting jelly)
E-270	Lactic acid (formed in the body, also the acid of soured milk)
E-280	Propionic acid (a fatty acid)
E-281	Sodium propionate
E-282	Calcium propionate
E-283	Potassium propionate
E-290	Carbon dioxide
296	Malic acid (a natural fruit acid)
297	Fumaric acid (a natural fruit acid)

Anti-oxidants: Compounds used to prevent fatty foods going rancid, and to protect the fat soluble vitamins (A, D, E and K) against the damaging effects of oxidation.

Vitamin C and derivatives

E-300	L-Ascorbic acid (vitamin C)
E-301	Sodium-L-ascorbate
E-302	Calcium-L-ascorbate
E-304	Ascorbyl palmitate

Vitamin E

E-306	Natural extracts rich in tocopherols (vitamin E)
E-307	Synthetic alpha-tocopherol
E-308	Synthetic gamma-tocopherol
E-309	Synthetic delta-tocopherol
E-310	Propyl gallate
E-311	Octyl gallate
E-312	Dodecyl gallate
E-320	Butylated hydroxyanisole (BHA)
E-321	Butylated hydroxytoluene (BHT)
E-322	Lecithins (lecithins occur naturally; their emulsifying properties are used when you add an egg to make mayonnaise)

More acids and their salts: Used as flavourings and as buffers to control the acidity of foods, in addition to other special uses.

Salts of lactic acid (E-270)

E-325	Sodium lactate
E-326	Potassium lactate
E-327	Calcium lactate

Citric acid and its salts

E-330 Citric acid (formed in the body, a natural fruit acid; as well as their properties as acids, citrates are often used as sequestrants (see *Glossary*) and emulsifying agents)

E-331	Sodium citrates
E-332	Potassium citrates
E-333	Calcium citrates

Tartaric acid and its salts

E-334	Tartaric acid (tartaric acid occurs naturally; as well as their properties as acids, tartrates are often used as sequestrants and emulsifying agents)
E-335	Sodium tartrate
E-336	Potassium tartrate (cream of tartar)

Phosphoric acid and its salts

E-338	Orthophosphoric acid
E-339	Sodium phosphates
E-340	Potassium phosphates
E-341	Calcium phosphates

Salts of malic acid (E-296)

350	Sodium malate
351	Potassium malate
352	Calcium malate
353	Metatartaric acid (used as a sequestrant in wine. Tartaric acid is E-334)
355	Adipic acid (naturally occurring)
363	Succinic acid (naturally occurring)
370	1,4-Heptonolactone
375	Nicotinic acid (a vitamin, also used to preserve the colour of some foods)
380	Triammonium citrate (an emulsifying salt; citric acid is E-330)
381	Ammonium ferric citrate (used to enrich bread with iron)
385	Calcium disodium EDTA (a sequestrant)

Emulsifiers and stabilizers: Used to enable oils and fats to mix with water, to give a smooth and creamy texture to food and slow the staling of baked goods. Many of these compounds are also used to form jellies.

Compounds E-400–416 are naturally occurring plant gums.

Alginates

E-400	Alginic acid (derived from seaweed)
E-401	Sodium alginate
E-402	Potassium alginate
E-403	Ammonium alginate
E-404	Calcium alginate
E-405	Propane-1,2-diol alginate

Other plant gums

E-406	Agar (derived from seaweed)
E-407	Carrageenan (derived from the seaweed Irish moss)
E-410	Locust bean gum (carob gum)
E-412	Guar gum
E-413	Tragacanth
E-414	Gum acacia or gum Arabic
E-415	Xanthan gum
416	Karaya gum
E-420	Sorbitol (a sweetener)
E-421	Mannitol (a sweetener)
E-422	Glycerol (a sweetener and humectant)

Fatty acid derivatives

430	Polyoxyethylene (8) stearate
431	Polyoxyethylene (40) stearate
432	Polyoxyethylene (20) sorbitan monolaurate (Polysorbate 20)
433	Polyoxyethylene (20) sorbitan mono-oleate (Polysorbate 80)
434	Polyoxyethylene (20) sorbitan monopalmitate (Polysorbate 40)
435	Polyoxyethylene (20) sorbitan monostearate (Polysorbate 60)
436	Polyoxyethylene (20) sorbitan tristearate (Polysorbate 65)

Pectin and derivatives

E-440(a)	Pectin (pectin occurs in many fruits, and is often added to jam, to help it to set)
E-440(b)	Amidated pectin
442	Ammonium phosphatides
E-450(a),(b),(c)	Sodium and potassium phosphates and polyphosphates (Phosphoric acid is E-338)

Cellulose and derivatives

E-460	Microcrystalline or powdered cellulose
E-461	Methylcellulose
E-463	Hydroxypropylcellulose
E-464	Hydroxypropyl-methylcellulose
E-465	Ethylmethylcellulose
E-466	Carboxymethylcellulose,sodium salt

Salts or esters of naturally occurring fatty acids

E-470	Sodium, potassium and calcium salts of fatty acids
E-471	Mono- and diglycerides of fatty acids
E-472	Various esters of mono- and diglycerides of fatty acids
E-473	Sucrose esters of fatty acids
E-474	Sucroglycerides
E-475	Polyglycerol esters of fatty acids
476	Polyglycerol esters of polycondensed esters of castor oil (polyglycerol polyricinoleate)
E-477	Propane-1,2-diol esters of fatty acids
478	Lactylated fatty acid esters of glycerol and propane-1,2- diol
E-481	Sodium stearoyl-2-lactylate
E-482	Calcium stearoyl-2-lactylate
E-483	Stearyl tartrate
491	Sorbitan monostearate
492	Sorbitan tristearate
493	Sorbitan monolaurate
494	Sorbitan mono-oleate
495	Sorbitan monopalmitate

Acids and salts used for special purposes: Buffers, emulsifying salts, sequestrants, stabilizers, raising agents, anti-caking agents.

Carbonates

500	Sodium carbonate, sodium bicarbonate (sodium bicarbonate is used as a raising agent in the kitchen)
501	Potassium carbonate, potassium bicarbonate
503	Ammonium carbonate
504	Magnesium carbonate (a very small amount of magnesium carbonate added to salt helps it to flow freely - it acts as an anti-caking agent. Magnesium is an essential dietary mineral)

Hydrochloric acid and its salts (ordinary salt is sodium chloride)

507	Hydrochloric acid
508	Potassium chloride (sometimes used as a replacement for ordinary salt)
509	Calcium chloride
510	Ammonium chloride

Sulphuric acid and its salts

513	Sulphuric acid
514	Sodium sulphate
515	Potassium sulphate (sometimes used as a replacement for ordinary salt)
516	Calcium sulphate
518	Magnesium sulphate

Alkalis: Used as bases to neutralize acids in foods.

524	Sodium hydroxide
525	Potassium hydroxide
526	Calcium hydroxide
527	Ammonium hydroxide
528	Magnesium hydroxide
529	Calcium oxide
530	Magnesium oxide (used as anti-caking agent)
535	Sodium ferrocyanide
536	Potassium ferrocyanide
540	Dicalcium diphosphate
541	Sodium aluminium phosphate

Compounds used as anti-caking agents, and for other uses

542	Edible bone phosphate (bone meal, used as a source of calcium in food enrichment)
544	Calcium polyphosphates (used as emulsifying agents)
545	Ammonium polyphosphates (used as emulsifying and texturizing agents in frozen chicken)

Silicon salts

551	Silicon dioxide (silica - sand; silicon may be an essential dietary mineral)
552	Calcium silicate
553	Magnesium silicate or trisilicate (talc)
554	Aluminium sodium silicate
556	Aluminium calcium silicate
558	Bentonite
559	Kaolin (fine white clay - aluminium silicate)
570	Stearic acid (a naturally occurring fatty acid)
572	Magnesium stearate

Gluconates

575	Glucono delta-lactone (gluconates are naturally occurring compounds)
576	Sodium gluconate
577	Potassium gluconate
578	Calcium gluconate

Compounds used as flavour enhancers
Glutamic acid and its salts

620	L-Glutamic acid (a natural amino acid)
621	Monosodium glutamate (MSG)
622	Monopotassium glutamate
623	Calcium glutamate

Nucleic acid derivatives

627	Sodium guanylate (naturally occurring)
631	Sodium inosinate (naturally occurring)
635	Sodium 5-ribonucleotide (naturally occurring)
636	Maltol (a sugar derivative)
637	Ethyl maltol
900	Dimethylpolysiloxane (used as an anti-foaming agent)

Compounds used as glazing agents

901	Beeswax
903	Carnauba wax
904	Shellac (used to wax apples)
907	Refined microcrystalline wax

Compounds used to treat flour and improve the texture of bread, cakes and dough

920	L-Cysteine hydrochloride (a natural amino acid)
924	Potassium bromate
925	Chlorine
926	Chlorine dioxide
927	Azodicarbonamide

Fats and oils

The fat in our diet is present in various forms: oils and fats added during food preparation or spread on bread, obvious fat that we can see in meat, and hidden fat such as that in the lean part of meat. There are even small amounts of oils in cereals. All these are chemically the same, by far the greatest part being neutral fats or triglycerides, with small amounts of other fats (phospholipids and cholesterol). They are all known collectively as *lipids*.

Triglycerides are nutritionally the most important, since the body can make as much phospholipid and cholesterol as it needs from the triglycerides and other components in the diet. Triglycerides consist of glycerol attached to three molecules of fatty acid. The fatty acids are chains of carbon atoms from 2 to 22 carbons in length, with an acidic group at one end. This end is attached to the glycerol. The shorter chains are liquid at room temperature, and the longer ones are solid. Chain length is one factor that determines whether the lipid is an oil or a solid fat. The other factor is how 'saturated' the fatty acid is.

Saturation means that all the carbon atoms in the chain carry their full quota of two hydrogen atoms and the carbons are linked by a single bond:

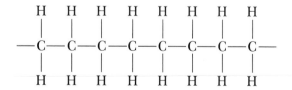

When one hydrogen is missing from two adjacent carbon atoms then they are linked by a double bond instead of a single bond, the fatty acid is called *mono-unsaturated*:

```
  H   H   H           H   H   H
  |   |   |           |   |   |
 —C — C — C — C = C — C — C — C—
  |   |   |   |   |   |   |   |
  H   H   H   H   H   H   H   H
```

If two or more pairs of hydrogen atoms are missing there will be two or more double bonds, and the fatty acid is *poly-unsaturated*:

```
  H   H           H           H
  |   |           |           |
 —C — C — C = C — C — C = C — C—
  |   |   |   |   |   |   |   |
  H   H   H   H   H   H   H   H
```

The less saturated the fatty acid, the lower its melting point.

Liquid oils can be hardened by hydrogenation, a process by which some of the double bonds become saturated with hydrogen. This is used to harden vegetable oils and fish oils in the manufacture of margarine.

Fats and oils are mixtures of different triglycerides, each of which can contain the same three or three different fatty acids of different chain length and different degrees of saturation. Usually one type of fatty acid tends to predominate, so the resultant mixture may be hard (e.g. lard and coconut fat) or soft (e.g. butter) or liquid (e.g. olive oil and sunflower oil). Cooking fats are specially blended to provide the right degree of softness, and other qualities. Fish oils consist of very long chain fatty acids (20 carbons and more), with four or five double bonds.

Strictly speaking, it is the fatty acids that are saturated or unsaturated, but it is common to refer to saturated, mono-unsaturated and poly-unsaturated fats.

Cis- and trans-

Poly-unsaturated fatty acids exist in two forms, which, although chemically only slightly different, have quite different physiological properties.

In one form all the chemical groupings are on the same side of the carbon chain. This is called the *cis*- form, and is the one that is physiologically active. When some of the groups are on opposite sides the fatty acid is *trans*- and behaves just like a saturated fat does.

Most of the natural poly-unsaturated fatty acids are of the *cis*- form, but when oils are hydrogenated for making margarine and cooking fats, some are changed into the *trans*- form.

The naming of fatty acids

The number of carbon atoms in a fatty acid can be between 4 and 22. It is almost always an even number; fatty acids with an odd number of carbon atoms are extremely rare. Each has a common (trivial) name and a formal chemical name. It is also possible to refer to them just by quoting the number of carbon atoms, followed by the number of double bonds, so that:

C18:0 would have 18 carbon atoms and no double bonds (stearic acid)

C18:1 would have 18 carbon atoms and one double bond (oleic acid)

C18:2 would have 18 carbon atoms and two double bonds (linoleic acid)

C18:3 would have 18 carbon atoms and three double bonds (linolenic acid)

Table 5 The common fatty acids

Name		C atoms	Double bonds
Short chain saturated fatty acids			
Butyric acid	C4:0	4	0
Caproic acid	C6:0	6	0
Caprylic acid	C8:0	8	0
Capric acid	C10:0	10	0
Medium chain saturated fatty acids			
Lauric acid	C12:0	12	0
Myristic acid	C14:0	14	0
Long chain saturated fatty acids			
Palmitic acid	C16:0	16	0
Stearic acid	C18:0	18	0
Arachidic acid	C20:0	20	0
Mono-unsaturated fatty acids			
Palmitoleic acid	C16:1	16	1
Oleic acid	C18:1	18	1
Poly-unsaturated fatty acids			
Linoleic acid	C18:2	8	2
Linolenic acid	C18:3	18	3
Arachidonic acid	C20:4	20	4

Collectively, the three poly-unsaturated fatty acids are called the essential fatty acids.

There is medical evidence that many people eat too much fat, and it would be beneficial to eat less, replacing some fatty foods with carbohydrate foods. In particular, it is thought that the saturated fats (saturated fatty acids) should be reduced. This would increase the proportion of our dietary fat that is poly-unsaturated. Therefore it is useful to consider not only the total amount of fat in a food, but the ratio of poly-unsaturated to saturated fat – the P/S ratio.

The P/S ratio for a number of foods is shown in Table 6.

Prepared foods like cakes, biscuits and pastry can be made with various types of fat, so the figures in Table 6 for the different classes of fatty acids in prepared foods can only be taken as a rough guide. We have assumed that a soft vegetable fat was used in making pastry; with omelette and scrambled egg we have assumed that butter was used.

No figures are given for fried foods. Obviously, the types of fatty acids will depend on the type of fat or oil the food was fried in, how much of the cooking fat is taken up by the food, and how much of the food's own fat is lost into the cooking fat. We have listed the fatty acid composition of some of the common types of cooking oil (numbers 291a-h) and margarines (numbers 260 a-c).

If the amount of fat in a food is expressed as a percentage of the weight of the food, the figure decreases or increases when the food takes up or loses water on cooking, or when it is dried.

For this reason it is preferable to express the fat as the percentage of the total energy in the food that is provided by fat. Since fat provides 9 kcal (37 kJ)/g, compared with 4 kcal (17 or 16 kJ)/g for protein and carbohydrate (see table 1 in *Food Tables*), the figure for the percentage of energy provided by fat is not the same as the percentage of fat by weight in the food.

The numbers for the foods in Table 6 are the same as were used for the foods in table 19 of *Food Tables*. We have not included any food that provides less than 0.5 g of fat/100 g of food, since that would make a negligible contribution to the diet.

The total of the amounts of saturated, mono-unsaturated and poly-unsaturated fatty acids in the food is always smaller than the total amount of fat, because the fat includes the glycerol (while the figures for fatty acids are for the free fatty acids without the glycerol). There may also be small amounts of other types of lipid, in addition to the triglycerides.

Table 6 The fatty acids in foods

		Fat g/100 g	% Energy from fat	Fatty acids g/100 g			
				Sat	Mono-unsat	Poly-unsat	P:S ratio
1	All-Bran breakfast cereal	2.5	8.7	1.0	0.8	3.0	3.0
2	Almonds	55	85	4.2	36.6	10.0	2.4
10	Avocados	20	90	2.6	17	1.9	0.7
11	Bacon, collar joint, raw	30	80	12	13	2	0.17
12	Bacon, collar joint, boiled	27	75	11	12	2	0.18
13	Bacon, gammon rashers, grilled	12	50	5	5.5	0.9	0.18
14	Bacon, gammon joint, raw	18	70	7.5	8	1.3	0.17
15	Bacon, gammon joint, boiled	19	65	7.5	8	1.3	0.17
16	Bacon rashers, streaky, raw	40	85	16	18	2.9	0.18
18	Bacon rashers, streaky, grilled	35	75	15	16	2.6	0.17
20	Barcelona nuts	65	90	4.6	50	6.7	1.5
21	Barley, pearl, raw	1.7	4	0.3	0.14	0.8	2.61
22	Barley, pearl, boiled	0.5	3.5	0.1	0.05	0.26	2.61
24	Beans, baked, canned in tomato sauce	0.5	7	0.08	0.05	0.25	3
25	Beans, broad, boiled	0.6	11	0.15	0.03	0.3	2
26	Beans, butter, raw	1	3	0.25	0.06	0.5	2
29	Beans, haricot, raw	1.5	5	0.25	0.15	0.8	3
30	Beans, haricot, boiled	0.5	5	0.1	0.05	0.3	3
32	Beans, mung, cooked (dahl)	4	35	2	1.1	0.1	0.05
33	Beans, red kidney, raw	1.7	5	0.3	0.17	1.0	3
36	Beef, brisket, raw	20	70	9.0	10	0.8	0.09
37	Beef, brisket, boiled	25	70	10	11	1.0	0.1
38	Beef, corned, canned	12	50	5	6	0.5	0.1
39	Beef, minced, raw	16	65	7	8	0.7	0.1
40	Beef, minced, stewed	15	60	6	7	0.6	0.1
41	Beef, rump steak, raw	14	60	6	6	0.5	0.08
43	Beef, rump steak, grilled	12	50	5	6	0.5	0.1
44	Beef, silverside, salted	14	50	6	7	0.6	0.1
45	Beef, sirloin, raw	23	75	10	11	0.9	0.1
46	Beef, sirloin, roast	21	70	9	10	0.9	0.1
47	Beef steak, stewing, raw	10	50	5	5	0.4	0.08

		Fat g/100 g	% Energy from fat	Fatty acids g/100 g			
				Sat	Mono-unsat	Poly-unsat	P:S ratio
48	Beef steak, stewing, stewed	11	45	5	5	0.4	0.08
49	Beef, topside, raw	11	55	5	5	0.45	0.1
50	Beef, topside, roast	12	50	5	5	0.45	0.1
56	Bemax	8	20	1	1	3.5	3.5
58	Biscuits, chocolate coated	27	45	17	8	1.1	0.06
59	Biscuits, cream crackers	16	32	2.7	2.2	8.5	3
60	Biscuits, plain digestive	20	37	8	7	1.6	0.2
61	Biscuits, chocolate digestive	24	42	12	9	1.6	0.13
62	Biscuits, semi-sweet	17	32	8	6	1.7	0.2
63	Biscuits, shortbread	26	45	15	8	1	0.07
64	Biscuits, wafers filled	30	49	18	9	0.9	0.05
65	Biscuits, water	12.5	24	2.3	1	7	3
68	Black pudding	22	65	10	7	0.2	0.02
69	Bloater, grilled	17	60	2.5	6.5	2.5	1
70	Bounty bar	26	50	17	4	0.6	0.04
71	Brain, boiled	9	60	2	2	1	0.5
72	Bran, wheat	5.5	23	1	0.7	3	3
73	Brazil nuts	60	90	16	20	23	1.4
74	Bread, brown	2.2	8.4	0.4	0.3	0.9	2
75	Bread, malt	3	11	0.8	0.5	1.2	1.5
76	Bread, white	1.7	6.2	0.4	0.25	0.7	1.8
77	Bread, white, toasted	1.7	4.8	0.4	0.25	0.7	1.8
78	Bread, wholemeal	2.7	10.7	0.5	0.4	1.1	2
79	Bread rolls, starch reduced	4	9	0.6	0.5	1.8	3
80	Bread rolls, white	7	19.7	1.8	1	2.8	1.5
81	Breadcrumbs, white	2	4.8	0.5	0.3	0.7	1.4
86	Buns, currant	8	23	2	1.3	3	1.5
87	Butter	82	99.7	50	26	2.2	0.04
94	Cake, fruit	11	30	4	5	1.7	0.4
95	Cake, Madeira	17	38	9	6	1.5	0.2
96	Cake, rock	16	35	6	7	2.5	0.4
97	Cake, sponge, with fat	27	50	10	11	4	0.4
98	Cake, sponge, without fat	7	20	2	2.5	0.8	0.4

		Fat g/100 g	% Energy from fat	Fatty acids g/100 g			
				Sat	Mono-unsat	Poly-unsat	P:S ratio
99	Cakes, various, fancy, iced	15	32	9	4	0.8	0.1
104	Cauliflower cheese	8	60	4	3	0.6	0.2
108	Chapatis, made with fat	13	34	6	4	1	0.17
109	Chapatis, made without fat	1	4	0.13	0.1	0.45	3.5
110	Cheese, camembert, soft type	23	69	14	7.4	0.6	0.04
111	Cheese, Cheddar, hard type	34	75	20	10.7	0.9	0.05
112	Cheese, cottage	0.5	7	2.5	1.3	0.1	0.04
113	Cheese, cream	47	97	28	15	1.3	0.05
114	Cheese, Danish blue	29	74	17.5	9	0.8	0.05
115	Cheese, Edam, semi-hard type	23	68	13.7	7.3	0.6	0.04
116	Cheese, Parmesan	30	66	17.7	9.5	0.8	0.05
117	Cheese, processed	25	72	15	8	0.7	0.05
118	Cheese, Stilton	40	77	24	13	1.1	0.05
121	Chestnuts	2.7	13.5	0.5	1	1	2
122	Chicken, raw, boned	4	30	1.4	1.9	0.7	0.5
123	Chicken, raw, meat and skin	18	70	5.9	8	2.7	0.5
124	Chicken, boiled, boned	7	35	2.4	3.3	1.1	0.5
125	Chicken, roast, boned	5	30	1.8	2.4	0.8	0.4
126	Chicken, roast, meat and skin	14	58	4.6	6	2.1	0.5
128	Chocolate, milk	30	50	18	10	1	0.05
129	Chocolate, plain	29	48	17	9	0.9	0.05
130	Christmas pudding	12	35	5	45	0.7	0.05
134	Cocoa powder	22	61	13	7	0.6	0.02
135	Coconut	36	92	31	2.4	0.6	0.02
136	Coconut, desiccated	62	92	53	4	1	0.02
137	Cod fillet, raw	0.7	8	0.13	0.06	0.3	2.3
138	Cod fillet, baked	1.2	11	0.2	0.13	0.5	2.5
141	Cod fillet, grilled	1.3	12	0.2	0.14	0.5	2.5
142	Cod fillet, poached	1	10	0.2	0.1	0.4	2
143	Cod fillet, steamed	1	10	0.15	0.1	0.3	2
144	Cornflakes, breakfast cereal	0.5	1	0.25	0.5	0.8	3
145	Cornflour	0.7	1.5	0.1	0.2	0.3	3
146	Cornish pastie	20	55	7	7	2	0.3

		Fat g/100 g	% Energy from fat	Fatty acids g/100 g			
				Sat	Mono-unsat	Poly-unsat	P:S ratio
147	Crab, boiled	5	36	0.6	1	1.9	3
148	Crab, canned	1	11	0.1	0.2	0.3	3
150	Cream, double	48	97	29	15	1.3	0.04
151	Cream, single	21	90	13	6.8	0.6	0.05
152	Cream, sterilized	23	90	14	7.5	0.6	0.04
153	Cream, whipping	35	95	21	11	1.0	0.05
154	Crispbread, rye	2	5	0.3	0.24	1.0	3.3
155	Crispbread, wheat	7.5	17	2.7	2	2.5	0.9
158	Custard, egg	6	44	3	2	0.3	0.1
159	Custard made with powder	4	30	2.6	1.4	0.1	0.04
163	Drinking chocolate powder	6	14	3.5	2	0.2	0.06
164	Dripping	100	100	43	48	4	0.1
166	Duck, raw, with skin	43	90	12	23	5	0.4
167	Duck, roast, with skin	10	47	8	16	3.5	0.4
168	Dumpling	12	50	6.50	4.2	0.3	0.05
171	Egg, raw, whole	11	67	3.4	43	1.2	0.35
173	Egg yolk	30	80	9.6	12	3.3	0.35
174	Egg, dried, whole	43	70	14	17	4.7	0.35
175	Egg, scrambled	23	84	11	8	1.4	0.13
179	Fish fingers, frozen	7.5	37	1.5	1	3.6	2.5
181	Fishcakes, frozen	0.8	6	0.2	0.1	0.4	2
182	Fish paste	10	55	2	1	5	2.5
183	Flour, brown	2	5	0.28	0.2	0.9	3.2
184	Flour, white	1.2	3	0.16	0.13	0.53	3.3
185	Flour, self raising	1.2	3	0.16	0.13	0.53	3.3
186	Flour, wholemeal	2	5	0.28	0.2	0.9	3.2
190	Fruit pie, individual	15	35	45	6	2	0.04
192	Goose, roast meat	22	63	7	10	2.50	0.4
200	Haggis, boiled	22	60	9	7	2	0.2
201	Halibut, raw	2.5	24	0.3	0.5	0.8	2.7
202	Halibut, steamed	4	27	0.5	0.9	1.4	2.8
203	Ham	5	38	1.9	2.3	0.5	0.26
206	Hare, stewed, with bones	6	38	2.4	1.1	1.9	0.8

		Fat g/100 g	% Energy from fat	Fatty acids g/100 g			
				Sat	Mono-unsat	Poly-unsat	P:S ratio
207	Heart, raw	4	32	2	1.3	0.3	0.15
208	Heart, roast	15	56	6	4	1.5	0.03
209	Heart, stewed	6	30	3	1.6	0.2	0.06
210	Herring, raw	19	72	3.7	9.3	3.3	0.9
212	Herring, grilled	13	60	2.6	6.5	2.3	0.9
214	Ice cream, dairy	7	35	4.3	1.7	0.15	0.03
215	Ice cream, non-dairy	8	43	4.2	3	0.6	0.14
218	Kidney, raw (ox)	3	30	1	1	0.1	0.1
220	Kidney, stewed (ox)	8	40	3	1.5	0.2	0.07
221	Kipper, baked	11	50	2.3	5.7	2	1.2
222	Lamb, breast, raw	35	80	17	13	1.6	0.09
223	Lamb, breast, roast	37	80	18	14	1.7	0.09
224	Lamb chops, raw	35	85	17	13	1.7	0.1
225	Lamb chops, grilled	29	75	14	11	1.4	0.1
226	Lamb cutlets, raw	36	85	18	14	1.7	0.09
227	Lamb cutlets, grilled	31	75	15	12	1.4	0.09
228	Lamb, leg, raw	19	70	9	7	0.9	0.1
229	Lamb, leg, roast	18	60	9	7	0.8	0.09
230	Lamb, scrag and neck, raw	28	80	14	11	1.3	0.09
231	Lamb, scrag and neck, stewed	21	65	10	8	1	0.1
232	Lamb, shoulder, raw	28	80	14	11	1.3	0.09
233	Lamb, shoulder, roast	26	75	13	10	1.2	0.09
234	Lard	100	100	42	42	9	0.2
240	Lemon curd (starch base)	5	15	2.4	1.5	0.2	0.08
241	Lemon sole, raw	1.4	16	0.2	0.3	0.5	2.5
243	Lemon sole, steamed	1	10	0.1	0.2	0.3	3
244	Lentils, raw	1	3	0.4	0.3	0.1	0.25
245	Lentils, boiled	0.5	4	0.2	0.15	0.05	0.25
248	Liver, raw (ox)	7	40	3	1.3	1.7	0.6
250	Liver, stewed (ox)	10	45	4	1.8	2.4	0.6
251	Lobster, boiled	3.5	25	0.40	0.65	1.25	3
253	Luncheon meat	27	80	10	13	2.3	0.2
254	Macaroni, raw	2	4.6	0.28	0.2	0.9	3.2

		Fat g/100 g	% Energy from fat	Fatty acids g/100 g			
				Sat	Mono-unsat	Poly-unsat	P:S ratio
255	Macaroni, boiled	0.6	4.4	0.08	0.06	0.27	3.4
256	Macaroni cheese	10	50	5	3	0.7	0.1
257	Mackerel, raw	16	65	4	6	4	1
260a	Margarine, hard, vegetable	81	100	30	38	10	0.33
260b	Margarine, soft, vegetable	81	100	26	34	18	0.7
260c	Margarine, poly-unsaturated	81	100	19	16	60	3.15
261	Margarine (low fat spread)	40	100	9.4	13	10	1.1
265	Mars bar	19	37	10	5	0.6	0.06
266	Marzipan	25	50	2	17	4.5	2.3
267	Matzo	2	4.5	0.3	0.15	0.9	3
268	Mayonnaise	79	99	10	47	8	0.8
271	Milk	3.8	52	2.2	1.2	0.1	0.05
273	Milk, Channel Islands	4.8	57	2.9	1.5	0.13	0.04
275	Milk, sweetened condensed	9	24	5.4	2.9	0.25	0.05
276	Milk, dried, skimmed	1.3	3	0.8	0.4	0.04	0.05
277	Milk, dried, whole	26	47	16	8.4	0.7	0.04
278	Milk, evaporated, whole	9	50	5.4	2.9	0.25	0.05
279	Milk, goat	4.5	56	3	1.2	0.14	0.05
280	Milk, human	4.1	53	2	1.6	0.3	0.15
281	Mincemeat	4	13	2	1.3	0.04	0.02
282	Muesli	7.5	18	1.3	2.7	3	2.3
285	Mussels, raw	2	27	0.3	0.4	0.5	1.7
286	Mussels, boiled	2	20.9	0.4	0.4	0.6	1.5
289	Oatmeal, raw	9	19	1.5	3	3.5	2.3
290	Oatmeal porridge	1	19	0.15	0.3	0.35	2.3
291a	Oil, coconut	100	100	85	6.6	1.7	0.02
291b	Oil, cottonseed	100	100	26	21.3	48	1.8
291c	Oil, corn	100	100	16	29.3	49.3	3
291d	Oil, olive	100	100	14	70	11.2	0.8
291e	Oil, palm	100	100	45	41.6	8.3	0.18
291f	Oil, peanut	100	100	19	48	28.5	1.5
291g	Oil, soya-bean	100	100	14	24	57	4.1
291h	Oil, sunflower	100	100	13	32	50	3.8

		Fat g/100 g	% Energy from fat	Fatty acids g/100 g			
				Sat	Mono-unsat	Poly-unsat	P:S ratio
293	Olives, pickled	9	95	1.2	6	1	0.8
294	Omelette	16	75	5	5	1.2	0.2
301	Oxtail, stewed	5	48	2	2.2	0.2	0.1
302	Pancakes	16	46	7	6	1.5	0.2
306	Pastry, flaky, cooked	40	63	13	15	5	0.4
307	Pastry, shortcrust, cooked	32	53	10	12	4.08	0.4
310	Peanut butter	54	77	9	23	13	1.4
311	Peanuts, fresh	50	77	9	23	14	1.6
312	Peanuts, salted roast	50	77	9	23	14	1.6
317	Peas, dried, raw	1.3	4	0.5	0.4	0.15	0.3
319	Peas, dried split, raw	1	3	0.4	0.3	0.1	0.25
321	Peas, chickpeas, raw	6	16	2.3	2	0.7	0.3
322	Peas, chickpeas, cooked	3.3	20	1.3	1	0.4	0.3
325	Pilchards, canned in tomato sauce	5	37	1.7	1.2	1.8	1.1
328	Plaice, raw	2.2	22	0.34	0.6	0.6	1.8
331	Plaice, steamed	2	19	0.3	0.5	0.5	1.7
337	Pork pie	27	65	9	11	3	0.3
338	Pork chops, loin, raw	30	80	12	13	2.3	0.2
339	Pork chops, loin, grilled	24	65	10	11	1.9	0.2
340	Pork, leg, raw	23	75	9	10	1.7	0.2
341	Pork, leg, roast	20	62	8	9	1.5	0.2
347	Prawns, boiled	2	16	0.2	0.3	0.7	3.5
350	Puffed Wheat	1.3	3.4	0.2	0.14	0.6	3
352	Quiche Lorraine	30	65	12.5	11	2.3	0.2
353	Rabbit, stewed	4	40	3	1.5	2.5	0.8
357	Ready Brek	9	19.8	1.5	3	3.5	2.3
361	Rice Krispies	0.7	1.6	0.5	0.5	0.7	1.4
362	Rice pudding, canned	2.5	23	2.5	1.3	0.1	0.04
363	Rice, raw	1	2	0.2	0.25	0.35	1.7
368	Salad cream	27	80	3.7	5	14	3.8
369	Salami	45	80	18	20	3.5	0.2
370	Salmon, raw	12	60	3	4.5	3	1
371	Salmon, canned	8	50	2	3	2	1

		Fat g/100 g	% Energy from fat	Fatty acids g/100 g			
				Sat	Mono-unsat	Poly-unsat	P:S ratio
372	Salmon, smoked	5	30	1	1.7	1	1
373	Salmon, steamed	13	60	3	5	3.3	1.1
374	Sardines canned in oil	14	60	2.7	7.5	2.7	1
375	Sardines canned in tomato	12	10	3	3	3.7	1.2
378	Sausage roll (flaky pastry)	36	70	14	16	4	0.3
379	Sausage roll (short pastry)	32	60	12	14	3.5	0.3
380	Sausage, liver sausage	27	80	8	11	2	0.25
381	Sausages, beef, raw	24	70	10	11	1	0.1
383	Sausages, beef, grilled	17	60	7	8	0.8	0.1
384	Sausages, frankfurters	25	85	10	11	2	0.2
385	Sausages, pork, raw	32	80	13	15	2.5	0.2
387	Sausages, pork, grilled	25	70	10	12	2	0.2
388	Sausages, saveloys, boiled	21	70	7	9	1.5	0.2
390	Scones	15	35	6	6	2.2	0.4
391	Semolina, raw	2	5	0.3	0.2	0.8	2.7
394	Shredded Wheat	3	8	0.4	0.3	1.3	3.3
395	Shrimps, boiled (peeled)	2.5	20	0.4	0.5	0.8	2
397	Soup, chicken	4	60	1	1.6	0.5	0.5
398	Soup, mushroom	4	70	2	1.3	0.3	0.15
399	Soup, oxtail	2	40	1	1	0.1	0.1
400	Soup, tomato	3	45	1	1	0.4	0.4
401	Soup, vegetable	1	20	0.1	0.1	0.6	6
402	Soya flour (full fat)	23.5	47	3.3	5.7	13	4
403	Soya flour (low fat)	7	20	1	1.7	4	4
406	Spaghetti, canned	0.7	10	0.1	0.1	0.4	4
407	Special K breakfast cereal	1	2	0.1	0.25	0.4	4
410	Sponge pudding	16	40	6	7	2.5	0.4
413	Steak, stewed, canned	13	65	5	6	0.5	0.1
415	Suet, shredded	87	95	50	32	1	0.02
416	Suet pudding	18	55	10	6.5	0.5	0.05
418	Sugar Puffs breakfast cereal	0.8	2	0.1	0.1	0.35	3.5
422	Sweet potato, raw	0.6	6	0.2	0.03	0.2	1
423	Sweet potato, boiled	0.6	6	0.2	0.03	0.2	1

		Fat g/100 g	% Energy from fat	Fatty acids g/100 g			
				Sat	Mono-unsat	Poly-unsat	P:S ratio
424	Sweetbread, raw	8	55	3	2.4	0.3	0.1
426	Sweetcorn, canned	0.5	6	0.08	0.1	0.2	2.5
427	Sweetcorn, kernels only	2	15	0.4	0.7	1.1	2.8
431	Toffees	17	35	9	5	0.4	0.04
437	Tongue, canned	17	75	6	7	1	0.2
438	Tongue, pickled, boiled	24	75	8	10	1.5	0.2
440	Treacle tart	14	35	5.5	6	1.8	0.3
441	Tripe, stewed	5	45	2	1.4	0.07	0.04
442	Trout, steamed	4.5	30	2	1.5	0.2	0.1
443	Tuna, canned in oil	22	70	4	9	8	2
444	Turkey, raw, meat only	2	20	0.8	0.6	0.7	0.9
445	Turkey, raw, meat and skin	7	45	2.4	1.8	2.3	1
446	Turkey, roast, meat only	3	20	0.9	0.7	0.9	1
447	Turkey, roast, meat and skin	6.5	35	2.2	1.7	2.1	1
451	Veal fillet, raw	3	25	1.1	1.3	0.1	0.1
452	Veal fillet, roast	12	45	4.8	5.5	0.50	0.1
453	Veal, jellied, canned	3	20	1	1.3	0.1	0.1
454	Venison, roast	6	30	4	1	0.01	0.003
455	Walnuts	52	88	6	8	35	6
458	Weetabix	3.5	9	0-5	0.4	1.5	3
462	Whiting, steamed	1	10	0.1	0.25	0.2	2
468	Yoghourt, flavoured	1	11	0.6	0.3	0.02	0.03
469	Yoghourt, natural	1	18	0.6	0.3	0.02	0.03
470	Yorkshire pudding	10	45	4.5	4	0.6	0.1

Glossary of food terms

Acerola. The fruit of a small bush native to the tropical and semi-tropical regions of America, *Malpighia punicifolia.* It is the richest known source of vitamin C, containing 1000 mg/100 g when ripe, and 300 mg/100 g when green. Also called West Indian, Barbados or Antilles cherry.

Abernethy biscuit. Biscuit made from flour, sugar, butter, eggs, milk and caraway seeds. Named after Dr John Abernethy (1764–1831) of St Bartholomew's Hospital, London.

Acesulphames. Class of synthetic non-nutritive sweetening agents; acesulphame-K is 130 times sweeter than sugar.

ACH Index. Arm, chest and hip index; a method of assessing nutritional status using the arm girth, chest diameter and hip width.

Additives. Chemicals, either natural or synthetic, added to foods to help in the manufacturing process, to preserve food and improve its taste and appearance. See page 9.

ADI. Acceptable Daily Intake: the total amount of any given food additive permitted by law. Usually one hundredth of the highest dose that shows no effect in tests. See page 9.

Aflatoxin. Toxic substances produced by the mould *Aspergillus flavus* growing on foods, especially nuts and grains stored under damp conditions.

Agar. A gum prepared from certain seaweeds used as an emulsifier and stabilizer in food processing (E-406). Also called agar- agar, Macassar gum, vegetable gelatine and Chinese gelatine.

Ageing. (1) A term applied to the oxidation of wheat flour, either by storage for several weeks or by adding chemicals that oxidize or 'age' the flour, enabling it to produce a more resilient dough.

(2) Ageing of wine refers to slow oxidation and other chemical changes with the development of a mellow flavour.

(3) In meat, ageing refers to the process of stiffening after killing (*rigor mortis*), followed a few days later by a softening process.

Alanine. A non-essential amino acid.

Aleurone layer. The single layer of large cells under the bran coat and outside the endosperm of cereals. Rich in protein and B vitamins.

Alginates. (E-400–405) Plant gums used as emulsifying agents, stabilizers and thickening agents.

Alimentary pastes. Pasta: shaped pieces of dough made from semolina or wheat flour and water, sometimes with the addition of egg and milk. The dough is partly dried in hot air, then more slowly, e.g. macaroni, spaghetti, noodles.

Allinson bread. A wholemeal loaf, named after Dr Allinson, who advocated its use in England at the end of the nineteenth century.

Amino acid, limiting. That essential amino acid present in a protein in least amount relative to the requirement.

Amino acids. The basic units from which proteins are formed. Twenty are commonly found in foods. Eight are essential, and must be provided in the diet in adequate amounts, since they cannot be made in the body: lysine, methionine, leucine, isoleucine, valine, threonine, phenylalanine and tryptophan. The remainder are not essential, since they can be made in the body as long as the total intake of protein is adequate: alanine, arginine, asparagine, aspartic acid, cysteine, glutamine, glutamic acid, glycine, histidine, proline, serine.

Amylases. Enzymes that hydrolyse starch to smaller molecules. Alpha-amylase gives small dextrin-like molecules, and beta-amylase (also known as diastase) gives maltose. The enzyme in saliva and pancreatic juice is alpha-amylase. Salivary amylase was formerly known as ptyalin.

Amylopectin. Starch consists of about 75–80% amylopectin, which is a branched chain of glucose units; the remaining 20–25% is straight chains of glucose units (amylose).

Amylose. The portion of starch which consists of straight chains of glucose units. See *Amylopectin*.

Aneurine. Old-fashioned name for thiamin (vitamin B_1).

Anorexia. Loss of appetite. Hence drugs used to reduce appetite are called anorectic drugs.

Anorexia nervosa. A psychological disturbance resulting in a refusal to eat, or restriction to a very limited number of foods.

Anthocyanins. A family of plant pigments; many are used as food colours (E-163).

Anti-vitamins. Substances that interfere with the function of vitamins, or destroy them. Thiaminase in some types of raw fish destroys thiamin (vitamin B_1); some drugs and some naturally occurring compounds interfere with the activity of vitamins.

Arginine. A non-essential amino acid.

Ascorbic acid. Vitamin C. Used in food processing (E-300) as an acid, preservative and anti-oxidant.

Ash, mineral. The inorganic (mineral) fraction of foods, determined either by heating to burn off organic compounds (protein, carbohydrate, fat, etc.) or by strong acid digestion of organic compounds.

Asparagine. A non-essential amino acid.

Aspartame. A non-nutritive sweetening agent 180 times sweeter than sugar. Chemically it is a synthetic dipeptide, aspartyl-phenylalanine methyl ester. Because aspartame contains the amino acid phenylalanine, and children with the rare genetic disease phenylketonuria must control their intake of this amino acid very strictly, foods containing aspartame are often labelled to note that they contain phenylalanine.

Aspartic acid. A non-essential amino acid.

Atwater factors. Numerical factors used to calculate the energy available from foods, allowing for losses due to both incomplete digestion and incomplete combustion of the nitrogen part of proteins. For carbohydrates and proteins the factor is 4 kcal/g (16 and 17 kJ/g respectively) and for fats it is 9 kcal/g (37 kJ/g). See also *Rubner factors*.

Autolysis. A process of self-digestion by enzymes naturally present in the food, e.g. the tenderizing of game by hanging to permit autolytic digestion of connective tissue; the softening and rotting of fruits and vegetables.

Available water. See *Water activity*.

Biotin. One of the B vitamins, sometimes called vitamin H.

Biuret test. A chemical test for proteins (actually their peptide bonds). A violet colour is produced when a drop of copper sulphate solution is added to a solution of the protein in alkali.

Blanching. Partial pre-cooking. Fruits and vegetables are blanched for a few minutes before freezing or drying to destroy enzymes that would otherwise cause spoilage.

Bloaters. Lightly salted, smoked herrings.

Body Mass Index. An index of obesity, also known as Quetelet's index, it is the weight (in kg) divided by the square of the height (in m). For adults, a value of 25 is normal, 25–30 is overweight and over 30 is defined as obesity.

Botulism. A rare form of severe food poisoning caused by the toxins produced by the bacterium *Clostridium botulinum*.

Bread, brown. Made from 85% extraction flour, and containing some of the bran and germ of the wheat.

Bread, granary. Made from a mixture of partially malted (sprouted) wheat and ordinary wheat flour and also some partially milled wheat grains.

Bread, wheatgerm. Made from ordinary white or brown flour with added wheat germ.

Bread, white. Made from 72% extraction flour, containing little or none of the bran and germ of the wheat.

Bread, wholemeal. Made from 100% extraction flour, containing all of the bran and germ of the wheat. *Stoneground* wholemeal flour is produced by the traditional milling process using stone mill wheels, and is generally coarser than wholemeal flour produced by modern milling methods. It may also contain small amounts of the sandstone used to make the mill wheels.

Browning reaction. The development of a brown colour in foods. The browning of the cut surface of fruit is due to the action of the enzyme phenol oxidase, and is called enzymic browning. Non-enzymic browning, or the Maillard reaction, is due to reaction between proteins and reducing sugars on heating or storage.

Buckwheat. A cereal, *Fagopyrum esculentum*, eaten as cooked grain or porridge, nutritionally similar to wheat, but not suitable for bread making.

Bulgur. One of the oldest known processed foods, originating in the Middle East. Wheat is soaked in water, cooked and dried, then lightly milled to remove the outer bran and cracked. It is eaten in soups and cooked with meat. Also known as ala and American rice.

Calorimetry. The measurement of heat production, either of foods or in activity. Indirect calorimetry involves calculation of heat production from the amounts of oxygen consumed and carbon dioxide produced.

Campden tablets. Sodium bisulphite (E-222) used as a preservative and to sterilize liquids and bottles.

Carageen (or carageenan) E-407. A gel extracted from seaweeds (usually Irish moss, *Chondrus crispus*, and *Gigarta stellata*) used to thicken products such as milk drinks, and as an emulsifying agent. Chemically it is a polysaccharide.

Caramel. E-150. Brown material formed by heating sugar in the presence of acid or alkali, used as a colour and flavour in a wide variety of foods and drinks. Also called burnt sugar.

Carob. Also known as the locust bean or St John's bread, the pods and seeds of *Ceratonia siliqua*. It contains a sweet pulp which is rich in sugar and plant gums. Carob gum is used as an emulsifier and stabilizer in food processing (E-410), and carob bean is used as an alternative to sugar in the production of some confectionery. Also used as an animal feed.

Carotenoids. E-160. A family of yellow, orange and red plant pigments, often used as food additives. Some are precursors of vitamin A.

Cassava (manioc). The tuber of the plant *Manihot utilissima*; the staple food in many tropical countries. It contains little protein and very little fat, and only 25 g starch/100 g, but gives very high yields under poor growing conditions.

Caviar(e). The salted hard roe of the sturgeon. It contains 30 g protein, 20 g fat, and no carbohydrate, yielding 340 kcal (81 kJ)/100 g.

Chapati. Flat unleavened Indian bread made from wheat flour or millet.

Cheese, full fat. Cheese made from full cream milk. Depending on the water content of the cheese, full fat cheeses may contain between 20–50% fat. Cheeses made from skimmed or partially skimmed milk contain less fat. See *Milk, skimmed*.

Chemical score. A method of defining the quality of a protein food; it is the ratio of the limiting amino acid expressed as a percentage of that amino acid in egg protein.

Cherry, West Indian. See *Acerola*.

Chitterlings. Intestines of ox, calf or pig.

Cholla. A loaf of white bread made in a twisted form (or Biblical beehive coil) from a large and small piece of dough plaited together. The dough contains egg and a pinch of saffron.

Cochineal. E-120. A red colour used in foods, obtained from an insect, the female conchilla (*Coccus cacti*).

Cock-a-leekie. Scottish soup made from leeks and chicken.

Coeliac disease (gluten-induced enteropathy). A severe digestive disorder due to sensitivity to the gliadin fraction of the protein, gluten, in wheat, rye and barley. The villi of the small intestine are seriously affected, and food is poorly absorbed. Treatment is by total exclusion of wheat, rye and barley from the diet. Maize and rice are tolerated.

Coenzymes. Substances needed to assist some enzymes in their functions. Most coenzymes are derived from one or other of the vitamins.

Complementation. A term used with respect to proteins, when a relative deficiency of one essential amino acid is compensated for by a relative surplus in another protein eaten at the same time.

Copra. Dried coconut, used for the production of coconut oil for manufacture of margarine, soap, etc.

Corm. The thickened underground base of the stem of certain plants, often called bulbs, e.g. onions, taro.

Corn. A general term for cereals. In the USA corn specifically means maize (*Zea mais*, sweetcorn, corn-cob).

Cornflour (corn starch). Purified starch from maize, almost pure starch. Used in custard and blancmange, and to thicken sauces and gravy.

Corn syrup. Glucose syrup prepared from starch, also contains other sugars and dextrins.

Cream of tartar. E-336. Potassium hydrogen tartrate, used together with sodium bicarbonate in baking powder. Also used in making boiled sweets to hydrolyse the sucrose to glucose and fructose (invert sugar). See *Sugar doctor*.

Custard powder. Usually cornflour flavoured with vanilla and coloured.

Cysteine. A non-essential amino acid. It is formed in the body from methionine, which is essential.

Cystic fibrosis. A genetic (inherited) disease which causes a disturbance of the glands that secrete the pancreatic digestive enzymes, so that food cannot be digested and absorbed properly. Treatment is by feeding predigested foods or supplementing the diet with pancreatic enzymes (pancreatin).

Cystine. A non-essential amino acid formed in proteins from cysteine.

Decaffeinated. Caffeine is a mild stimulant present in tea and coffee. It can be removed during manufacture by a variety of chemical extraction procedures. If the caffeine is removed by extraction with water, the tea or coffee is sometimes called 'naturally' decaffeinated.

Dextrins. A mixture of soluble compounds formed by the partial breakdown of starch by heat, acid or enzymes, as when bread is toasted. Complete breakdown of starch and dextrins yields maltose and glucose.

Dextrose. An alternative name for glucose. Commercially, the term 'glucose' is often used for corn syrup, a mixture of glucose, other sugars and dextrins; pure glucose is called dextrose.

Dhal. Indian term for dried split peas of various kinds, e.g. the pigeon pea (*Cajanus indicus*), khesari (*Lathyrus sativus*). Red or Massur dhal is the lentil (*Lens esculenta*).

Diastatic activity. A measure of the ability of flour to hydrolyse some of its own starch to maltose needed for growth of the yeast during fermentation of the dough.

Disaccharides. Sugars consisting of two monosaccharide units, e.g. sucrose (ordinary table sugar), maltose, lactose.

Dietary fibre. See *Fibre, dietary*.

Diet-induced thermogenesis. The increase in metabolism, measured as an increase in heat production, following the ingestion of food, and believed to be due to the activation of brown adipose tissue. Also called the specific dynamic action of food.

DNA. Deoxyribonucleic acid. The genetic material found in the nuclei of all cells. Chemically it consists of the sugar deoxyribose, together with phosphates and purine and pyrimidine bases.

Douglas bag. An inflatable bag used for collecting expired air to determine the energy used in activities by measuring oxygen used and carbon dioxide produced (the process of indirect calorimetry).

Durum wheat. A hard type of wheat of the species *Triticum durum* (most bread wheats are *Triticum vulgare*), used for the production of semolina intended for the preparation of pastas.

E- . Prefix for reference numbers of food additives permitted throughout the European Community. See page 10.

e. On a food label the letter 'e' signifies that this is a package size that has been declared to the European Community as a standard size.

Elemental diet. A defined diet formula prepared from purified amino acids, peptides, glucose, etc., which requires little digestion and leaves minimal residue. Used in oral and tube feeding.

Emulsifying agents. Substances that aid the uniform dispersion of oil in water, as in margarine, ice cream, salad cream, etc. Emulsifying agents include plant gums, carageen, alginates, lecithin, egg yolk and soaps. Substances that maintain these emulsions in a stable form are called stabilizers, and include cellulose derivatives, alginate derivatives, egg albumin, super-glycerinated fats and lecithin.

Enrichment. The addition of vitamins, mineral salts and sometimes amino acids to increase the nutritional value of a food.

Enteral nutrition. Feeding with a liquid diet directly into the stomach or small intestine using a fine tube passed through the mouth or nose.

Erythorbic acid. The D-isomer of ascorbic acid, with little or no vitamin activity, used in food processing as an anti-oxidant. Also known as D-araboascorbic acid.

Essential amino acids. Those amino acids that cannot be made in the body, but must be provided in the diet in appropriate amounts. See *Amino acids*.

Essential fatty acids. The poly-unsaturated fatty acids that cannot be made in the body and are required in the diet. See page 16.

Essential oils. Volatile odorous oils found in plants (e.g. lemon oil and orange oil in the peel) and used as flavours. They bear no relation to the edible oils, which are triglycerides. See *Flavedo* and page 16.

Ester. Chemical name for the compound formed by reaction between an acid and an alcohol. Many esters have pleasant fruity flavours and aromas.

Extraction rate. The yield of flour when wheat is milled. Wholemeal flour is 100% extraction rate; white flour is usually 72%.

Fat, animal. Any fat prepared from animal sources, normally the body fat (suet, lard or dripping).

Fat, non-milk. Foods such as ice cream may be prepared with full cream milk and added cream,

when they are called Dairy Ice Cream, or with other animal or vegetable fats added to the milk.

Fat, vegetable. Vegetable oils and fats may be either from a single plant (e.g. see page 24) or mixtures of different vegetable oils.

Fats, high ratio. Shortenings with a high proportion of mono- and diglycerides, i.e., superglycerinated. They disperse into doughs more readily, and allow a higher ratio of sugar to flour than does ordinary shortening. See also *Flour, high ratio*.

Ferrum redactum. Latin name for reduced iron, metallic iron in a finely divided form, prepared by the chemical reduction of iron oxide. Sometimes used to enrich foods such as bread.

Fibre, crude. A term used in food analysis for the residue after food has been extracted successively with petroleum ether, dilute sulphuric acid and sodium hydroxide under specified conditions, minus the mineral ash. Used mainly in calculating the food value of animal feedstuffs, and not related to dietary fibre.

Fibre, dietary. Collective term for the structural parts of plant tissues that are not digested by human digestive enzymes; includes cellulose, hemicelluloses, pectins, gums and lignin. Formerly known as roughage or bulk.

Fibre, soluble. Some of the hemicelluloses, pectins and gums are soluble in water and have physiological effects that differ from those of insoluble fibre. Soluble fibres are found largely in fruits, vegetables, oats and pulses, insoluble fibre mainly in wheat products.

Flavedo. The coloured outer peel layer of citrus fruits, also called epicarp or zest. Contains the oil sacs with the essential oils.

Flavonoids. One of the groups of pigments in flowers, fruit, vegetables and tree bark. Other plant pigments are anthocyanins and carotenoids.

Flavoproteins. A group of oxidizing enzymes containing specific proteins plus riboflavin (vitamin B_2).

Flour, extraction rate. Wholemeal flour is 100% extraction rate: it contains all of the wheat grain. Removal of the bran and germ during milling gives flour with a lower extraction rate. Brown flour is 85% extraction and white flour is 72% extraction. See also *Bread*.

Flour, high ratio. Flour of very fine and uniform particle size, treated with chlorine to reduce the strength of the gluten. Used for making cakes, since it is possible to add about twice as much sugar (140 parts to 100 parts of flour) as can be incorporated into ordinary flour.

Folic acid. One of the B vitamins. Also called folacin or pteroylmonoglutamic acid.

Frangipani (frangepane). Originally a jasmine perfume which gave its name to an almond cream flavoured with the perfume, and to cakes and pastry filled with an almond-flavoured mixture.

Freeze drying. Also called lyophilization. A method of dehydrating (drying) foods in which the material is frozen, then subjected to high vacuum. The ice sublimes as water vapour without melting. If the frozen food is warmed during the process, this is termed accelerated freeze drying (AFD).

Frumenty. An old English dish made from whole wheat stewed in water for 24 hours, until the grains burst and set in a thick jelly, then boiled with milk.

Gastrin. The hormone secreted by the stomach under the influence of certain foods, especially meat, and by distension of the stomach. The hormone enters the blood stream and stimulates the secretion of gastric juice.

Gelatin. A water-soluble protein prepared by boiling collagen (the protein of connective tissues in animals) or bones. It has a poor nutritional value since it lacks tryptophan and some other essential amino acids. Dilute solutions of gelatin set to a firm jelly on cooling, and it is widely used as a thickening or gelling agent in food manufacture, as well as in table jellies and as a decorative glaze on savoury dishes. Aspic is a gelatin jelly flavoured with lemon, tarragon vinegar, sherry, peppercorns and vegetables.

Ghee. Clarified butter fat made by heating butter and separating the water.

Glucose syrups. Concentrated solutions of hydrolysed starch, consisting of glucose, maltose and other sugars, used in sugar confectionery. They may be prepared from maize or potato starch, by the action of acid and/or enzymes. Also called corn syrup, starch syrup and confectioners' glucose.

Glucose tolerance. The ability of the body to deal with a test dose (usually 50–75 g) of glucose. Used as a test for diabetes. In healthy people blood glucose rises from the fasting level of 80–100 mg/100 ml to about 150 mg/100 ml, and returns within 1–1.5 hours; in diabetics it rises much higher, and remains high for much longer.

Glutamic acid. A non-essential amino acid. The mono-sodium salt, monosodium glutamate (MSG) is used as a flavour enhancer (E-621).

Glutamine. A non-essential amino acid.

Gluten. One of the proteins of wheat, rye and barley, which gives dough its special elastic properties. Patients with coeliac disease react specifically to gluten, and must avoid gluten-containing foods.

Goitrogens. Substances found in a number of foods, including members of the cabbage family, cassava and peanuts, which interfere with the normal function of the thyroid gland, and may cause goitre if eaten in excessive amounts.

Graham bread. Wholemeal bread in which the bran is very finely ground, as advocated by the American miller Graham in 1837.

Gram, Indian. A general name for small dried peas, e.g. green gram (*Phaseolus aureus*), black gram (*Phaseolus mungo*, the mung bean), red gram (*Cajanus indicus*).

Grape sugar. An alternative name for glucose.

Gum acacia. A plant gum is used as an emulsifier and stabilizer in food processing (E-414). Also known as Gum Arabic.

Gums. Soluble dietary fibre from various plant seeds or exudates and seaweeds, frequently used as emulsifiers and stabilizers in food processing (E-400, E-416). Most are not digested.

Haggis. A traditional Scottish dish made from liver, heart and lungs of sheep, cooked with suet, oatmeal and seasoning, and boiled in a bag made from sheep's stomach.

Haslet. An old English country dish made from pig's heart, liver, lungs and sweetbread cooked in small pieces with seasoning and flour.

Histidine. A non-essential amino acid, but essential to babies.

HTST. High Temperature–Short Time treatment to sterilize food with maximum efficiency and anti-microbial effect, and minimum damage to the food and its nutrients.

Hydrogenated oils. Liquid oils are hardened by treatment with hydrogen in the presence of a catalyst, when some of the double bonds are saturated with hydrogen (see page 16). Used to make margarines and cooking fats from oils.

Inanition. Exhaustion and wastage due to complete lack of food or to non-assimilation; a state of starvation.

Inositol. So-called meat sugar, a hexa-hydro derivative of cyclohexane which occurs in cell membrane phospholipids. It is an essential dietary factor for insects, some animals and micro-organisms, but not for human beings.

Intermediate moisture foods. A method of preserving foods while retaining their texture, by reducing the water available to spoilage organisms. This is achieved by adding glycerol and a little salt, and cooking at about 70°C. The moisture content may be 15–50%, but the 'water activity' is low.

International units. Before vitamins and other natural substances such as hormones were purified, their biological potency was determined in standardized, but arbitrary, 'units'. Nowadays they are measured in terms of weight (but vitamins A and D are sometimes quoted in i.u.).

Inulin. A polysaccharide found in Jerusalem artichoke, chicory root and some other tubers as the storage carbohydrate, the equivalent of starch. However, chemically it is a polymer of fructose units, rather than glucose, and is not digested by human enzymes.

Invert sugar. A mixture of glucose and fructose produced by the hydrolysis of sucrose. Originally so-called because the mixture inverts the plane of rotation of polarized light relative to that produced by sucrose. Invert sugar is important in confectionery manufacture because 10–15% prevents sucrose from crystallizing. It is 130% as sweet as sucrose. See *Sugar doctor*.

Isinglass. A protein (essentially pure collagen) from the swim bladder of the sturgeon, used to clarify beer and wine, since it precipitates slowly, carrying down small suspended particles.

Isoleucine. An essential amino acid.

Jaggery. A coarse dark sugar made from the sap of the coconut palm, or from sugar cane juice. Also known as gur.

Junket. The precipitated protein of milk, prepared by treatment with the enzyme rennin. Frequently sweetened and flavoured to produce a dessert.

Kelp. Any one of several species of the large brown seaweed *Laminaria*. Occasionally used as a food or food ingredient, but of no nutritional value except as a minor source of iodine.

Ketchup (or catsup or catchup). From the Chinese *koechap*, originally meaning a brine of pickled fish, now used for any spicy sauce of fruit or vegetable juice (e.g. tomato ketchup).

Ketone bodies. Products of fatty acid metabolism (including acetone) which accumulate in the blood in fasting and in diabetes, and are found in the breath and urine.

Kippers. Lightly salted herrings, smoked overnight (see also *Bloaters*).

Kjeldahl determination. A method of determining the nitrogen in a food, as an index of the protein content. The food is digested with sulphuric acid, when all the nitrogenous compounds are converted to ammonia, which can be measured easily. For most foods, protein = N (determined this way) x 6.25.

Kwashiorkor. A form of protein-energy malnutrition in which the severe muscle wastage is hidden by oedema. See also *Marasmus*.

Laver. Edible seaweed of the family *Porphyra*; made into laver bread by boiling, mincing, mixing with oatmeal and frying.

Lean body mass. That part of the body weight which excludes the fat (adipose) tissue, i.e. muscle, organs and bones.

Lecithins. Phospholipids, i.e. compounds of glycerol, fatty acids, phosphate and choline. Important in the body in cell membranes and for fat transport in the bloodstream. Not a dietary essential, since they can be made in the body. Used in food manufacture as emulsifying agents.

Lectins. Toxic substances found in many legumes which cause red blood cells to agglutinate (hence they are also called phytohaemagglutinins). Destroyed by several minutes rapid boiling.

Leucine. An essential amino acid.

Low fat foods. Foods prepared with a lower fat content than is traditional, although there is no legal definition. Low fat cheeses and yoghurts are prepared using skimmed or partially skimmed milk, low fat sausages and meat products using leaner cuts of meat than is usual.

LRNI. Lower Reference Nutrient Intake. An amount of the nutrient below which it is likely that most people's requirements will not be met. Only 2.5% of the population have a requirement lower than the LRNI. The range between the LRNI and the Reference Nutrient Intake (RNI) is the range of intakes which will meet the requirements of 95% of the population. See also RDA and RNI.

Lycopene. A red pigment found in tomatoes, pink grapefruit and other foods. Chemically it is a carotene derivative, but it has no vitamin A activity.

Lymph. The fluid between the blood vessels and the tissues. Essentially blood plasma, it transports nutrients from the blood to tissues, and waste products from tissues back to the bloodstream for excretion.

Lysine. An essential amino acid.

Maillard reaction (Non-enzymic browning). A chemical reaction between the amino acid lysine in proteins and reducing sugars, producing a brown colour when foods are heated or stored. Although the lysine becomes unavailable, the product often has an improved flavour, as in roasted meat and toasted bread.

Malt. A mixture of the products of breakdown of the starch of wheat or barley grains, mainly the sugar maltose, prepared by extraction from sprouted grains.

Mangelwurzel (also called mangoldwurzel or mangold). The root of *Beta vulgaris rapa*, a cross between red and white beet, used as cattle feed.

Manioc. See *Cassava*.

Manna. A dried exudate of the tamarisk (manna-ash) tree, *Fraxinus ornus*, containing mannitol and a variety of other sugars. Thought to have been the food eaten by the Israelites in the wilderness. Alternatively, a product of the manna lichen (*Lecanosa*), which forms fluffy light balls during drought.

Maple syrup. The sap of the sugar maple tree, *Acer saccharum*, containing mainly sucrose.

Marasmus. Protein-energy malnutrition with severe muscle wastage and, in children, very poor growth.

Menadione. Vitamin K_3.

Menaphthone. Vitamin K_3.

Menaquinones. Vitamin K_2 series.

Methionine. An essential amino acid.

Milk, long-life (UHT – ultra-high-temperature milk). A commercial name for milk that has been sterilized by heating to a high temperature (137°C) for a very short time (2 s). This causes little change in flavour, and allows the milk to be stored (unopened) for a considerable time.

Milk, malted. A preparation of dried milk with extract of malt and flour.

Milk, skimmed. Full cream milk contains 3.8 g fat/100 g (or 4.8 g/100 g in Channel Islands milk). If all of the cream is removed, the product is skimmed milk, containing only 0.1 g fat/100 g. Partially skimmed milk has some of the cream removed, leaving 1.5–2 g of fat/100 g.

Miracle berry. The fruit of the West African bush *Richardella dulcifera* which contains a protein ('miraculin') that causes sour foods to taste sweet.

Molasses. The dark uncrystallizable residue left after repeated crystallization of sugar from cane. It contains 500 mg iron/100 g, and traces of other minerals as well as sucrose, glucose and fructose.

Monosaccharides. Single sugars such as glucose, fructose, galactose and the pentose sugars.

Monosodium glutamate. See *Glutamic acid*.

Niacin. Nicotinic acid, one of the B vitamins.

Nicotinamide. One of the vitamers of nicotinic acid.

Nicotinic acid. One of the B vitamins – this and nicotinamide are the recommended names.

Ninhydrin test. A chemical test for the amino groups of amino acids and proteins, which give a pink or purple colour with the chemical ninhydrin.

Nitrogen conversion factor. The numerical factor used to calculate the protein content of a food from the amount of nitrogen it contains, ranging from 5.7 to 6.25, depending on the amino acid composition of the protein. For the mixture of proteins in the diet the factor of 6.25 is usually used. See also *Protein, crude*.

Offal. (1) A corruption of 'off-fall'. With reference to meat, offal is those parts that are cut away to yield the carcase, i.e. the liver, heart, kidneys, brain, spleen (melts), lungs (lights), tripe, tongue, pancreas (sweetbreads) and other organs. Also called organ meats.

(2) With reference to cereals, offal means the bran and germ discarded when wheat is milled to white flour.

Oils, fixed. The triglycerides or edible oils (see page 16), as opposed to the volatile or essential oils.

Olestra. Trade name for a non-digested fat substitute made from sucrose polyester (SPE) intended for use in food manufacture and preparation.

Oligosaccharides. Carbohydrates composed of 3–10 monosaccharide units; two monosaccharides form a disaccharide, while more than four form a polysaccharide.

Organic. Chemical substances containing carbon (apart from simple carbonate and cyanide salts) are organic, since they frequently come from living matter, unlike inorganic mineral salts.

Organic foods. More correctly, organically grown. Vegetables grown without the use of chemicals such as pesticides, fungicides and chemical fertilizers, and not treated with preservatives. 'Organic meat' is from animals fed on organically grown plants, without the use of growth promoters and using only a limited number of medicines to treat diseases.

Organoleptic. The combination of the senses of taste (as perceived by the mouth) and aroma (as perceived by the nose). Also called sensory perception.

Osmophiles. Micro-organisms, frequently yeasts, that can grow in high concentrations of sugar or salt (i.e. in jams and brine pickles that have a high osmotic pressure).

Osmotic pressure. A measure of the concentration of compounds that attract water, and hence render it unavailable to micro-organisms.

Pancreatin. A preparation of pancreatic digestive enzymes used to treat the digestive disorder of cystic fibrosis and other diseases of pancreatic insufficiency.

Pantothenic acid. One of the B vitamins.

Papain. A proteolytic enzyme from the juice of the pawpaw (papaya, *Carica papaya*), used to tenderize meat. Also known as vegetable pepsin.

Parenteral nutrition. Feeding by direct infusion of nutrients into the veins. Used as a supplement for seriously ill patients, and as the sole source of nutrition (total parenteral nutrition) when intestinal function is deranged by disease.

Pasteurization. Mild heat treatment, sufficient to destroy many pathogenic (dangerous) bacteria, but not enough to sterilize food by killing all micro-organisms. It prolongs the storage life of the food for a limited period, with less effect on flavour, texture and nutrients than the higher temperatures needed to sterilize completely. Named after Louis Pasteur, who invented the process.

Pemmican. Dried powdered meat in fat, formerly used as a concentrated food on expeditions.

Pepper (1) Sweet pepper – paprika, capsicum, bell pepper or pimento, the fruit of the annual plant *Capsicum annuum*. Used fresh in salads and dried as a spice (paprika).

(2) Red pepper, chilli (chili) or cayenne pepper – the very pungent fruit of *Capsicum frutescens*.

(3) Black and white pepper (peppercorns) – the pungent fruit of the climbing vine *Piper nigrum*. This is ordinary table pepper.

Permitted additives. Only those food additives that are permitted by law may be used in foods, so the term 'permitted' is unnecessary. See page 9.

Phenylalanine. An essential amino acid.

Phenylketonuria. A rare genetic disease in which the essential amino acid phenylalanine is not metabolized normally. Brain development is severely affected, but can be normalized by strict control of the intake of phenylalanine.

Phosphatase test. For the completeness of pasteurization of milk. The enzyme phosphatase, normally present in milk, is inactivated by treatment at a temperature only slightly higher than is required to destroy the tubercle bacillus and other pathogens. This test can detect the presence of as little as 0.2% raw milk in a pasteurized sample.

Phosphatides. An alternative name for phospholipids.

Phospholipids. Fatty substances composed of fatty acid and glycerol linked to one of a variety of phosphate-containing compounds (e.g. lecithin). Important in cell membranes and in fat transport in the blood, but not dietary essentials. In the diet they yield the same 9 kcal (37 kJ)/g as other fats.

Phylloquinone. Vitamin K_1.

Phylloxera. An aphid that destroyed many of the vineyards of Europe in the nineteenth century.

Many splendid varieties of vine were saved by grafting onto resistant American root-stock; many Spanish and Portuguese vineyards escaped, and still raise 'pre-phylloxera' varieties.

Pica. A psychiatric term for perverted appetite, especially eating earth, clay, sand, paper, etc.

Plankton. Minute organisms, both plants (phytoplankton) and animals (zooplankton) drifting in the sea, which serve as the basis of the food chain.

Polenta. Traditional Italian porridge made from maize meal.

Polyphosphates. Complex inorganic phosphate salts added to foods, especially meat and poultry, to prevent discoloration (e.g. in sausages), aid mixing of fat and retain water and so improve texture.

Proline. A non-essential amino acid.

Proof spirit. A method of describing the alcohol content of spirits, based originally on the ability of the spirit to ignite gunpowder. In Britain, proof spirit contains 57.07% alcohol by volume (49.24% by weight), and spirits were described as under-proof (less than this amount of alcohol) or over-proof. Thus, 70 degrees proof (UK) is 70% of proof spirit, or 40% alcohol by volume. Note that American proof is different (see *Food Tables*, table 2).

Protein conversion factor. See *Nitrogen conversion factor*.

Protein, crude. Defined as N content x 6.25.

Protein-energy ratio. The proportion of the energy yield of a food provided by protein.

Provitamin. A substance that is converted in to the active vitamin in the body; 7-dehydro-cholesterol is provitamin D; beta-carotene was known as provitamin A.

Proximate analysis. Analysis of the major constituents of food – protein, fat, carbohydrate.

P/S ratio. The ratio of poly-unsaturated/saturated fatty acids in a food. See page 17.

Psychrophilic bacteria. Bacteria that grow under cold-store conditions, down to temperatures as low as -10°C. Below this temperature, growth stops, but organisms survive and will recommence growth when the temperature rises.

Ptyalin. Obsolete name for the enzyme amylase found in saliva.

Pyridoxine. Vitamin B_6. (Pyridoxal and pyridoxamine are also biologically active.)

Quetelet's Index. See *Body Mass Index*.

Quorn®. Trade name (Rank Hovis MacDougal) for a protein-rich material prepared by growing fungi on starch. Used in vegetarian dishes, it has a fibrous structure which gives it a chewiness, and can be flavoured to resemble meat or fish. See also *Textured vegetable protein*.

Raffinose. An indigestible trisaccharide, composed of fructose, glucose and galactose, found in many legumes, especially soya. It is fermented by intestinal bacteria, and causes flatulence. See also *Stachyose*.

Rape. A vegetable, *Brassica napus*, closely related to the garden swede, also known as cole or coleseed. Grown as a source of edible oil; rape is the only oil-seed plant that grows well in cold climates.

RDA. Recommended Dietary (or Daily) Amount (or Allowance) of a nutrient. An amount more than adequate to meet the requirements of almost all members of the population. Tables of RDA and RNI (Reference Nutrient Intake) show recommended amounts for different groups of the population; for labelling purposes a single figure is used to show the nutrient composition of the food as per cent of RDA. This is an average figure based on the number of people in each group of the population. See also *RNI*.

Red herrings (Yarmouth bloaters). Herrings that have been salted and smoked for about 10 days. See also *Bloaters* and *Kippers*.

Reducing sugars. Sugars that will chemically reduce Fehling's solution or Benedict's reagent because they have a free aldehyde or ketone group. They include glucose, fructose, lactose and pentoses.

Reference man and woman. An arbitrary physiological standard, defined as being 25 years old, healthy, living in a temperate climate with a mean annual temperature of 10°C. The reference man weighs 65 kg and requires 3200 kcal (13.5 MJ)/day; the reference woman weighs 55 kg and requires 2300 kcal (9.7 MJ).

Reference protein. A theoretical 'perfect' protein that can be used with 100% efficiency in the body, at whatever level it is fed in the diet; in practice the efficiency of protein use falls as the intake increases. The reference protein is used to express recommended intakes.

Rennet. Extract of calf stomach containing the enzyme rennin, used to clot milk in cheese making and for junket. Plant enzymes such as bromelain from pineapples and ficin from figs are sometimes called vegetable rennet and are used in the manufacture of 'vegetarian' cheese.

Resistant starch. The component of starch that has been gelatinized by heat and is resistant to digestion; it is included with dietary fibre in food analysis. It is not clear whether it acts physiologically in the same way as dietary fibre.

Respiratory quotient (RQ). The ratio of carbon

dioxide produced / oxygen consumed. The oxidation of carbohydrate in the body gives a respiratory quotient of 1.0; fat metabolism gives 0.71 and protein 0.8.

Respirometer. Apparatus to measure the consumption of oxygen and production of carbon dioxide, and so permit calculation of energy utilization – the process of indirect calorimetry, as opposed to direct calorimetry, where the output of heat is measured.

Retinol. Vitamin A.

Rheology. The science of the deformation and flow of matter, e.g. the plasticity and brittleness of fats, doughs, etc.

Riboflavin. E-101. Vitamin B_2.

Rice paper. Smooth white film ('paper') made from the pith of a tree peculiar to Taiwan. It is edible, and is used as a base in baking macaroons, etc.

Rice, wild. *Zizanie aquatica*, also known as American wild rice, Indian rice, Tuscarora rice and zizanie. Native to eastern North America; the plant grows 12 feet high, producing a long thin greenish grain containing 14% protein (more than ordinary rice), 7% fat and 74% carbohydrate. Little is grown, so it is an expensive gourmet food.

RNI. Reference Nutrient Intake. An amount of the nutrient calculated to be more than adequate to meet the requirements of almost all members of the population. The range between the Lower Reference Nutrient Intake (LRNI) and the RNI is the range of intakes which will meet the requirements of 95% of the population. See also *RDA* and *LRNI*.

Roller dryer. Equipment for drying liquid food mixtures by spreading a film over heated rollers from which the dried food is scraped off. The process causes little nutritional damage, but there is more loss of vitamin C and thiamin than in spray drying.

Roller mill. Used to mill wheat to flour; a pair of horizontal cylindrical rollers revolve at different speeds, so that the grain is crushed and ground in a single operation.

Rope. Bacteria of the species *Bacillus mesentericus* and *B. subtilis* occur on wheat, and so in flour. They form spores that can survive baking, and then are present in the bread. In warm and moist conditions the spores germinate, and the bacterial mass converts the bread into sticky yellowish patches which can be pulled out into rope-like threads - hence the term 'ropy bread'. Can be inhibited by the addition of acids.

Royal jelly. The food on which bee larvae are fed to cause them to develop into queen bees rather than workers. Claimed, without any evidence, to have a rejuvenating effect on human beings.

Rubner factors. Factors used to calculate the energy content of foods after allowing for losses of urinary nitrogen from proteins, but not allowing for incomplete digestion and absorption, as do the Atwater factors. Protein 4.1 kcal/g (17.2 kJ), fat 9.3 kcal (38.9 kJ), carbohydrate 4.1 kcal (17.2 kJ).

Saccharin. A non-nutritive sweetener, chemically benzoic sulphimide, 550 times sweeter than sugar, discovered in 1879.

Sago. Starchy grains prepared from the pith of the sago palm, *Metrozylon sago*. Almost pure starch, with only 0.5% protein, negligible fat and traces of B vitamins.

Salmonella. A genus of bacteria that cause the commonest form of food poisoning. Destroyed by adequate heating, common in poultry.

Salt. Chemically the product of reaction between an acid and an alkali. Common table salt is sodium chloride.

Saltpetre. Potassium nitrate, used in curing (pickling) meats.

Saponification. Splitting of fat into its constituent fatty acids and glycerol by heating with alkali.

Saponins. A group of substances extracted from plants that produce a 'soapy' lather with water. Used as foam producers in beverages, and to emulsify oils.

Sauerkraut. Pickled cabbage. Cabbage preserved by a lactic fermentation. In the presence of 2–3% salt, acid-forming bacteria thrive and convert the sugars of the cabbage to acetic and lactic acids, which act as preservatives.

Scombroid poisoning. Food poisoning caused by bacterial spoilage of the scombroid family of fish, including mackerel, tunny and sardines.

Scurvy grass. A herb, *Cochlearia officinalis*, which was recommended as far back as the late 16th century as a remedy for scurvy (vitamin C deficiency).

Semolina. The inner, granular, starchy endosperm of hard or durum wheat, not yet ground into flour. Used to make pasta and semolina milk pudding.

Sequestrants. Substances that combine with metal ions or acid radicals and render them inactive, e.g. citrate, tartrates, EDTA (ethylene diamine tetra-acetic acid, also known as versene or sequestrene). Used to remove traces of metals that might cause food to discolour or deteriorate.

Serine. A non-essential amino acid.

Shaddock. Alternative name for the pomelo, *Citrus grandis*, from which the grapefruit is descended. Named after Captain Shaddock, who introduced it into the West Indies.

Shortening. Soft fats that produce a crisp, flaky baked product. The fats are plastic, unlike oils, and disperse as a film through the batter, and prevent the formation of a hard tough mass. Shortenings are compounded from mixtures of fats, or prepared by hydrogenation of oils. Lard has the required properties without modification.

Siderosis. Accumulation of the iron-protein complex haemosiderin, in tissues, when the diet is abnormally rich in iron, or in diseases where there is excessive destruction of red blood cells, from which the iron is liberated.

Single cell protein. A collective term for the biomass of bacteria, algae or yeasts (and also, incorrectly, for moulds and fungi) potentially useful as animal or human food.

Solanaceae. The family of plants that includes the potato (*Solanum tuberosum*), aubergine (*S. melongena*), Cape gooseberry (*Physalis peruviana*) and tomato (*Lycopersicon esculentum*).

Solanine. A heat-stable toxic glycoside occurring in small amounts in potatoes, and increased when potatoes are exposed to light and turn green. These larger amounts cause gastro-intestinal upset.

Solids-not-fat. The solids of milk, excluding the fat (cream), i.e. the protein, lactose and salts.

Sorbitol. A six-carbon sugar alcohol formed by the reduction of fructose, also known as glucitol and glycitol. It is metabolized as carbohydrate, yielding 4 kcal (17 kJ)/g, but it is only slowly absorbed from the intestine, and is tolerated by diabetics. Occurs naturally in some fruits.

Sorghum. A cereal, *Sorghum vulgare*, that thrives in semi-arid regions, and is an important food in tropical Africa and Asia. Also known as kaffir corn, guinea corn, jowar and millo maize. Contains 10 g protein, 3 g fat, 70 g carbohydrate, 4.5 mg iron/100 g.

Soxhlet. A laboratory apparatus for extraction from solids; solvent is continuously percolated through the material. Used particularly to extract fat from foods for analysis.

Specific dynamic action. The increase in metabolism (measured by increased heat output) following the ingestion of food, nowadays called diet-induced thermogenesis, and believed to be due to stimulation of brown adipose tissue.

Spirit, silent. Highly purified alcohol distilled from any fermented material.

Spirometer. Alternative name for respirometer.

Spirulina. A blue-green alga living in lakes that can fix atmospheric nitrogen. It has been eaten for centuries by people living in Mexico and around Lake Chad in Africa, and recently sold in the West as a (rare) vegetable source of vitamin B_{12}.

Spray dryer. Equipment in which the material to be dried is sprayed in fine droplets into a hot air chamber, and falls to the bottom as a dry powder. There is very little damage to the food, since the time of heating is very short.

Stachyose. An indigestible tetrasaccharide sugar containing fructose, glucose and two galactose molecules, found in many legumes, especially soya. It is fermented by intestinal bacteria, and causes flatulence. Also called mannotetrose and lupeose. See also *Raffinose*.

Staple food. The principal food in a diet.

Starch, modified. Starch that has been altered by chemical or physical treatment to change its gel strength, flow properties, clarity, stability of paste, etc.

Starter. Culture of bacteria used to inoculate or start growth in a fermentation, e.g. in milk for cheese production.

Sugar. Ordinary sugar is chemically sucrose; it may be prepared from sugar cane or sugar beet. Crude sugar crystals are Muscovado or Barbados sugar, moist and dark brown. Refining yields a lighter brown crystal, Demerara sugar, and finally white sugar. London Demerara sugar is white sugar which has been coloured light brown.

Sugar doctor. An additive used to prevent crystallization or 'graining' of sugar in confectionery, e.g. invert sugar, starch syrup or a weak acid, such as cream of tartar, which hydrolyses some of the sucrose to invert sugar.

Superglycerinated fats. Ordinary fats are triglycerides (see page 16); mono- and diglycerides are termed superglycerinated. Glyceryl monostearate is a solid at room temperature, flexible and non-greasy; it is used as a plasticizer to soften the crumb of bread, to reduce spattering in frying fats, as an emulsifier and stabilizer and as a protective coating for foods.

Sweeteners, bulk. Carbohydrates and carbohydrate derivatives used to replace sugar and glucose syrups. Less sweet than sugar, and hence required in relatively large amounts compared with artificial (intense) sweeteners.

Sweeteners, non-nutritive (Intense sweeteners). Compounds which are very many times sweeter than sugar. Saccharin, cyclamate and acesulphame have no food value at all; aspartame is used in such small amounts that it has negligible food value.

Tapioca. Starch globules prepared from the root of the cassava plant.

Textured vegetable protein. Spun or extruded vegetable protein, commonly derived from soya, flavoured to imitate meat or other foods.

Therapeutic diets. Specially formulated to treat diseases or metabolic disorders.

Thermoduric. Micro-organisms that are resistant to heat, but do not prefer high temperatures (these are thermophilic organisms). They survive pasteurization temperatures. Not usually pathogens, but they may be indicative of insanitary conditions.

Thermophilic.Micro-organisms that preferentially live at high temperatures.

Thiamin. Vitamin B_1.

Threonine. An essential amino acid.

Trace elements. Mineral salts needed in small amounts (micrograms or milligrams per day), such as iodine, copper, manganese, magnesium, zinc, etc., as distinct from those minerals needed in hundreds of milligrams per day (e.g. sodium, potassium, calcium). Iron lies between these two groups.

Tragacanth. A plant gum used as an emulsifier and stabilizer in food processing (E-413).

Tripe. The lining of the stomach of ruminants, usually calf or ox. Largely connective tissue, which is converted into gelatine on boiling; 9 g protein, 3 g fat /100 g.

Triticale. A hybrid between wheat (*Triticum*) and rye (*Secale*) that combines the winter hardiness of rye with the special properties of wheat grain.

Tryptophan. An essential amino acid. A precursor of the vitamin niacin.

Turmeric. The dried rhizome of *Curcuma longa*, a member of the ginger family, used to colour foods yellow and as a condiment (e.g. in curry powder and mustard picallili). The pigment is used as the dye curcumin (E-100).

Tyrosine. A non-essential amino acid.

UHT milk. Ultra high temperature treatment. See *Milk, long-life*.

Valine. An essential amino acid.

Vanaspati. Hydrogenated vegetable oil, similar to margarine, and usually fortified with vitamins A and D.

Vitamers. The different (related) chemical forms of a vitamin, which can be converted in the body to the active vitamin.

Vitamins. Organic compounds that are essential in small amounts for normal health and metabolism. They cannot be made in the body, and must be provided by the diet (except for niacin, which can be made from tryptophan, and vitamin D which can be made in the skin).

Water activity. An index of the extent to which the water in a food is available to micro-organisms; the presence of water-holding substances such as sugar, salt or glycerol reduces the water activity, and so prevents growth of micro-organisms. The water activity of a food is the ratio of the vapour pressure of the water in the food / the vapour pressure of pure water at the same temperature.

Xanthan gum. A complex polymer made by bacterial fermentation, which forms a gel, used as a thickening agent in some foods (E-415).

Zizanie. See *Rice, wild*.